What's a Real Doctor?

Cherice Roth

Fulton Books, Inc.
Meadville, PA

Published by Fulton Books 2021

ISBN 978-1-63710-313-5 (paperback)
ISBN 978-1-63710-314-2 (digital)

Printed in the United States of America

This book is dedicated to Jeremy, Tristan, and Cooper. Thank you for giving me a reason to be a better wife, mom, and human every day.

Clara's dad and Tristan and Cooper's mom drop them off at school.

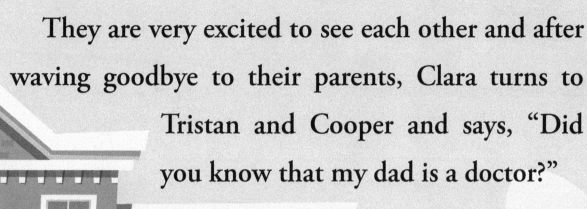

They are very excited to see each other and after waving goodbye to their parents, Clara turns to Tristan and Cooper and says, "Did you know that my dad is a doctor?"

Tristan and Cooper reply together, "Our mom is a doctor too!"

3

4

Clara replies, "But my dad is a *real* doctor."

Tristan and Cooper look at each other and reply, "Our mom is a veterinarian."

Clara thinks for a moment then asks, "Is that a real doctor?"

Cooper replies, "Of course it is," and crosses his arms.

Clara thinks hard and says, "Well, my dad went to school for a *long* time and studied *really* hard."

Tristan replies, "Yep, our mom did that too."

Cooper says, "Our mom gives shots to her patients to make sure they stay well."

Clara replies, "My dad does that too!"

8

9

Tristan says, "Our mom figures out what's wrong and knows how to fix it."

Clara replies, "Yep, my dad does that too."

Clara says, "My dad lets patients and their families know if they need surgery."

Cooper says, "Mom does that too!"

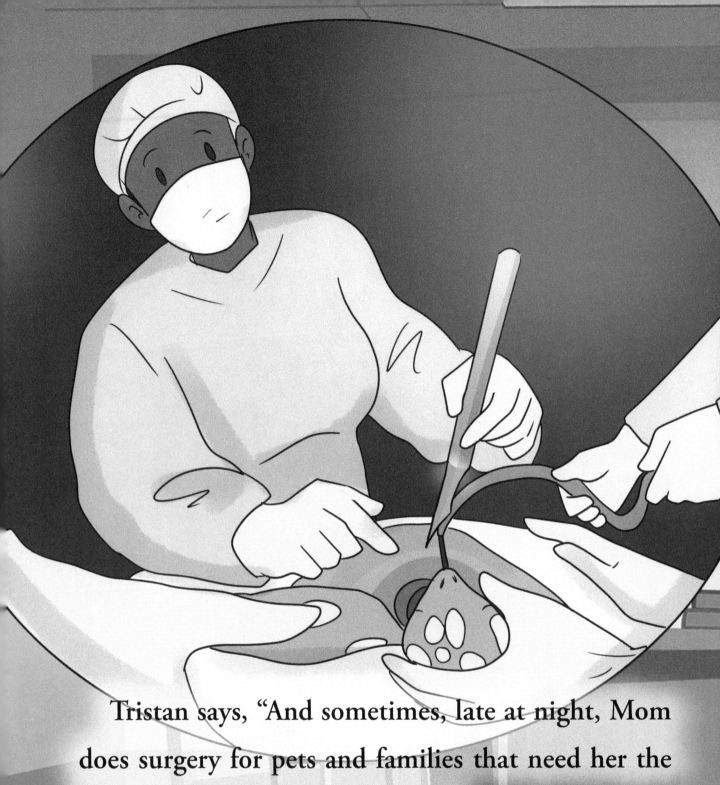

Tristan says, "And sometimes, late at night, Mom does surgery for pets and families that need her the most. No matter what critter it is!

Clara stops and thinks for a moment. "Oh! My dad doesn't do that...*but* after they have surgery, my dad makes sure they feel better by writing prescriptions for medicine.

Tristan replies, "Yep, Mom does that too!"

Cooper chimes in, "Mom also checks on them after they are healed to make sure they are all better."

Clara says, "My dad does that too!"

Clara says, "You're right, Tristan and Cooper, your mom *is* a real doctor, just like my dad.

Cooper smiles and says, "Yes! Our mom is just a little bit cooler because she gets to doctor every animal."

At the end of the school day, the kids say goodbye to each other, and Clara gets in the car, and her dad is driving.

Clara says, "Dad, Tristan and Cooper's mom is a real doctor too! Just like you."

Dad replies, "Yes, she is, but she works on animals, so she's a little bit cooler than me."

About the Author

Dr. Cherice Roth is a graduate of Texas A&M College of Veterinary Medicine. Before veterinary school, she earned a Master's Degree from the University of North Texas Health Science Center in Biochemistry. Before becoming a veterinarian, she was a college instructor. She spent time perfecting her exotic animal medicine and surgical knowledge in Australia and, upon returning to the US, mentored and guided veterinary assistants and DVMs in her home hospitals, while helping to develop and implement ongoing client-education programs more broadly. She has held many roles within veterinary medicine from Texas A&M student ambassador up to Chief Veterinary Officer. Her most important roles are that of a mom and a wife. Outside of work, you can find her in the woods of Oregon with her many, many "Roth Ranch" animals, her sons (The Rothlings), and husband, or serving to help make veterinary care accessible for all critters.

CPSIA information can be obtained
at www.ICGtesting.com
Printed in the USA
BVHW020511200422
634742BV00001B/4